Comprehen

Ages 6–7

Irene Yates

HOPSCOTCH
EDUCATIONAL PUBLISHING

Published by Hopscotch
A division of MA Education Ltd
St Jude's Church
Dulwich Road
Herne Hill
London SE24 0PB

Tel: 020 7738 5454

© 2007 MA Education Ltd

Written by Irene Yates
Series design by Blade Communications
Illustrated by Catherine Ward
Printed in the UK by CLE, St Ives, Huntingdon, Cambridgeshire

ISBN 1-905390-01-7
ISBN13 978-1-905390-01-4

Irene Yates hereby asserts her moral right to be identified as the
author of this work in accordance with the Copyright, Designs
and Patents Act, 1988.

The National Literacy Strategy Framework – Text level links for Ages 6–7

	T1	T2	T3	T4	T5	T6	T7	T8	T9	T10	T11	T12	T13	T14	T15	T16	T17	T18	T19	T20	T21	T22	T23	T24	T25	T26	T27
Term 1 Activity 1a		•																									
Activity 1b		•																									
Activity 1c		•																									
Activity 2a				•																							
Activity 2b				•																							
Activity 2c				•																							
Activity 3a								•																			
Activity 3b								•																			
Activity 3c								•																			
Activity 4a						•																					
Activity 4b						•																					
Activity 4c						•																					
Activity 5a					•																						
Activity 5b					•																						
Activity 5c					•																						
Activity 6a													•														
Activity 6b													•														
Activity 6c													•														
Activity 7a														•													
Activity 7b														•													
Activity 7c														•													
Term 2 Activity 8a				•																							
Activity 8b				•																							
Activity 8c				•																							
Activity 9a						•																					
Activity 9b						•																					
Activity 9c						•																					
Activity 10a																			•								
Activity 10b																			•								
Activity 10c																			•								
Activity 11a																		•									
Activity 11b																		•									
Activity 11c																		•									
Activity 12a							•																				
Activity 12b							•																				
Activity 12c							•																				
Activity 13a			•																								
Activity 13b			•																								
Activity 13c			•																								
Activity 14a					•																						
Activity 14b					•																						
Activity 14c					•																						
Term 3 Activity 15a					•																						
Activity 15b					•																						
Activity 15c					•																						
Activity 16a								•																			
Activity 16b								•																			
Activity 16c								•																			
Activity 17a						•																					
Activity 17b						•																					
Activity 17c						•																					
Activity 18a	•																										
Activity 18b	•																										
Activity 18c	•																										
Activity 19a																•											
Activity 19b																•											
Activity 19c																•											
Activity 20a													•														
Activity 20b													•														
Activity 20c													•														
Activity 21a																		•									
Activity 21b																		•									
Activity 21c																		•									
Activity 22a																	•										
Activity 22b																	•										
Activity 22c																	•										

'Comprehension is the ultimate goal of reading'
Primary Framework for Literacy – September 2006

This book explores the 'Understanding and Interpreting Texts' and the 'Engaging with and Responding to Texts' strands of the renewed *Primary Literacy Framework*. It is also cross-referenced to the Literacy Strategy's text level objectives. These text level objectives are the basis for the activities in this book. The book is not intended as an individual workbook. Its concept is that an adult will be working with the child, at whichever stage, in order to facilitate their understanding and their ability to process and answer the questions, simultaneously developing their reading and writing skills as they work through the pages.

Each activity should be discussed, with the child verbalising what they understand from the pictures or the texts, the adult pointing out what they miss and encouraging them to verbalise answers to the questions before attempting to write or having the adult scribe for them.

As the adult goes through the text with the child, she should encourage the child to become familiar with and recognise the various features of words: initial sounds, digraphs, double and triple consonants, vowels, final sounds and so on, and help the child to a) build up words and b) predict words from knowledge of some of the graphic details and from the context. In this way the activities become much more than just a comprehension task and help the child to absorb the many strategies that they may use in learning to read.

It is important for the children to learn to form their answers in simple but full sentences – ie those with at least a subject and a verb. They will then assimilate from this early stage that this is the way to answer comprehension questions.

The following notes give guidance for each activity.

Activity 1, Y2 (Year), T1 (Term), T2 (Text level)
1a – Read the text to and with the children. Encourage them to predict, from the meaning, which word might come next. Sound beginnings and endings of words and discuss meanings.
1b – Read the text to and with the children. Talk about what word might come next, where appropriate. Discuss meanings and whether their predictions make sense.
1c – Share the reading with the children. Stop at intervals to encourage predictions of words. Give beginning sounds and endings where appropriate to help with prediction.

Activity 2, Y2, T1, T4
2a – Read to and with the children. Discuss how events in a story happen one after another and how

time passes. Ask them to guess how much time the contest will take.
2b – Read to and with the children. Discuss how time passes in a story. What words can help to show this?
2c – Share reading with the children. Discuss the element of time in stories. Discuss the idea of events happening one after another. Discuss the fact that the contest is an event. How does the text show that time does not stand still?

Activity 3, Y2, T1, T8
3a – Read the poems to the children. Give them copies and ask them to join in with you where they can read or remember the words. Encourage them to find other animal poems, copy them and add to the collection.
3b – Read the poems to and with the children. Explain the idea of a collection or anthology (a set, of poems for example). Make a compilation.
3c – Read the poems with the children. Discuss the idea of an anthology or collection and ask them to look for more animal poems so that they can compile an anthology.

Activity 4, Y2, T1, T6
4a – Read the text to and with the children. Discuss times when they have not been very well and help them to identify with the story.
4b – Read the story together. Ask the children to discuss what it is about and whether it has any links with their own lives.
4c – Encourage the children to read the story and discuss how they can identify with the main character. Which other stories have they read where they have found links with their own lives?

Activity 5, Y2, T1, T5
5a – Read the text to and with the children. Discuss what a plot in a story is. Ask them how one event in the plot of this story leads to another.
5b – Share the story with the children. Discuss the word 'plot' as in a story. Discuss how events in a plot are about action and consequence.
5c – Encourage the children to tell you the plot of the story. Discuss how a plot is made up of events happening in an action and consequence sequence. How does this pertain to this text?

Activity 6, Y2, T1, T13
6a – Ask the children to verbalise what they can see on the page until they have talked through the full set of instructions. Help them to carry out the instructions.
6b – Talk about the need for instructions to be clear and in the right order. Help the children to work through the text so that they know exactly what they have to do.
6c – Share the reading with the children. Get them to check that everything that is needed is there and that

all the tasks are in the right order. Ask them to follow the instructions.

Activity 7, Y2, T1, T14

7a – After reading the text together, ask the children to tell you what they think a list is. Help them to work out the different features of a list, ie that there is always a common factor; that they may be written in alphabetical order, size order, time order, priority order; that a list is used to help you to remember something; that it is usually written down the page.

7b – Ask the children to verbalise what they have read and discuss with them what kinds of lists they know or have read, and what the important features of those lists might be, as above.

7c – Ask the children to read the text and then verbalise to you exactly what they think a list is, what it is for and how it might be arranged, using the features as above.

Activity 8, Y2, T2, T4

8a – Read the text to and with the children. Help them to read the questions and verbalise their answers. The story has a predictable end. How do they know what that ending will be?

8b – Read the text to and with the children. What do they think will happen? What is it about the text that makes them think so?

8c – Ask the children to tell you what the story is about. What do they think will happen? What is it in the text that makes them think this?

Activity 9, Y2, T2, T6

9a – Talk about the picture and the text. Discuss the idea of character in a story. Ask the children how they can identify which character is which from the words of the text.

9b – Talk about the picture and the text. Discuss the idea of character in a story. Ask the children to describe the different characters. How do they know, from the text, how to do this?

9c – Discuss the text and the idea of character. Can the children identify and describe the characters, using words from the text?

Activity 10, Y2, T2, T19

10a – Read the diagram to and with the children. Can they identify its different parts? Make sure they understand what its cyclical element portrays.

10b – Discuss the idea of a cyclical diagram with the children. Is every step of the transformation explained in a clear way? How useful do they think a cyclical diagram is for explaining things?

10c – Discuss how the concept of a cyclical diagram works. Do they have to start at one place? What happens if they start reading the diagram at any other place on it? Can they think of other events they might make a cyclical diagram for?

Activity 11, Y2, T2, T18

11a – Read the text to and with the children. Ask them for other instances of alphabetically ordered texts. Why do they think a text works in this way?

11b – Share the text with the children. Ask them to find other examples of indexes and find out if they are always in alphabetical order. Is this a good idea? Why?

11c – Discuss the idea of an index in particular and of alphabetically ordered texts in general. How does putting the ideas into alphabetical order help the reader of the information book?

Activity 12, Y2, T2, T7

12a – Read the story to and with the children. Ask them to tell you the story in their own words, making sure they have it all in the right order, and then retell it to someone else.

12b – Share the story with the children. Make a list together of the important things that are in it and ask them to retell the story from the list. Is everything in the right order?

12c – Discuss the idea of retelling the story, making sure that the sequence is right and that the dialogue is included. Give opportunities for this.

Activity 13, Y2, T2, T3

13a – Talk with the children about what a theme might be in a story. It is what a story is about. Can they identify the common thread or theme of all of these stories?

13b – After sharing reading, discuss the idea of theme in a story. What is the shared theme of all of these stories? Could the children suggest an idea for another story using the same theme?

13c – After reading through the text and the questions, ask the children to talk about what a theme in a story is. The shared theme in these four stories is 'animals' but each story also has a theme of its own, one being 'escape'. What do the children think the others are?

Activity 14, Y2, T2, T5

14a – Read the text to and with the children. Discuss the idea of a setting, that is where and when a story is set. Encourage the children to verbalise the setting in the text.

14b – Share the text with the children. Discuss what a setting in a story is. What can they tell you about this setting?

14c – Ask the children to tell you what the setting is for this text. Why is setting important to a story? How does it help to make a beginning? Could the children follow up this setting with a plot of their own?

Activity 15, Y2, T3, T5

15a – Read the text to and with the children. Make sure they understand the word 'author'. Discuss the information given about this 'famous' author.

15b – Read the text together. Discuss the idea of information about authors given in books. Ask the children to look for instances of author information in some of the books available in the school and compare them.

15c – Encourage the children to read the text, to verbalise and discuss it and then to look for, and share, information about other authors which may be given in some of their classroom books.

Activity 16, Y2, T3, T8

16a – Read the poem to and with the children, asking them to join in where they can read or remember the words. Talk about the words or phrases that stand out to them as particularly humorous and try to work out why this is.

16b – Share the poem with the children. Discuss parts of the poem that they find particularly fun and get them to talk about why the words have such an effect on them.

16c – Ask the children to read the poem to themselves silently and then to read it aloud together. Which parts of the poem particularly make them laugh or they think are funny? How do they think the words work to give this effect?

Activity 17, Y2, T3, T6

17a – Read the poem to and with the children. Ask them to give you an instant response to it. Nothing they say can be wrong; they should just verbalise how the poem makes them think and feel. Read the poem several times to see if their responses change when they become more familiar with it.

17b – Share the poem with the children. Give them time to assimilate it and to think about it. Ask them to share their responses with the group – how does the poem make them feel? What pictures does it give in their heads?

17c – Ask the children to read the poem silently and then aloud together. How does the poem make them feel? What do they see in their imagination? How does the poem relate to their experiences?

Activity 18, Y2, T3, T1

18a – Share and guide the children through the reading of this text. Get them to focus on phonetic awareness, spellings and syllables. Make a list of any new words that they encounter.

18b – Share and guide the children through the reading of the text. Get them to investigate any words with similar spelling patterns but different sounds. Make a list of any new vocabulary.

18c – Ask the children to look for words with common spelling patterns, prefixes or suffixes and to list any new vocabulary they encounter.

Activity 19, Y2, T3, T16

19a – Read the text to and with the children. Discuss the idea of scanning – looking at the text with a focus

of certain words or phrases in the head so that you find them easily. Give them several words to focus on and find quickly.

19b – Read the text to and with the children. Discuss the concept of scanning. Give the children several words and phrases to scan the text for.

19c – Encourage the children to read the text thoroughly and then to scan for certain words, phrases and subheadings.

Activity 20, Y2, T3, T13

20a – Read the text to and with the children. Ask them to describe to you verbally the difference between fiction and non-fiction. Give them examples of books in the room and ask them to decide which they are.

20b – Share the text with the children. Encourage them to verbalise what they think the differences are between fiction and non-fiction. Ask for examples.

20c – When the children have read the text, discuss the concepts of fiction and non-fiction. Ask them to give you as many features as they can of a) fiction and b) non-fiction. Give them opportunities to pick up a book and tell you straight away which it is and how they know.

Activity 21, Y2, T3, T18

21a – Read the text to and with the children. Discuss what kind of writing it is and what it is trying to tell them. Ask the children to decide how useful the text is for its purpose.

21b – Share the text with the children. Discuss what kind of writing they think it is and what it should be setting out to do. How useful do they think it is for that purpose?

21c – Encourage the children to read the text and decide what kind of writing it is and what they should be able to get from it. How useful do they think it is for its purpose? Try this with some different kinds of text.

Activity 22, Y2, T3, T17

22a – Read the text to and with the children. Discuss with them the idea of skimming, that is reading swiftly, picking out the main ideas. How easily can they skim this text to find out what it is about?

22b – Share the text with the children. Explain to them the concept of skim-reading. Encourage them to skim the text and verbalise what they have picked up. Have they omitted important things?

22c – Encourage the children to read the text. Explain the concept of skim-reading. Can they skim the text and make a verbal list of all of its main features? Give them the opportunity to do this with another piece of text.

Name _____

Frogs ahoy!

Here are the Frog family. Mum, Dad, Big Brother, Little Brother and Baby Sister. They love to spend the day sitting in the sunshine, dipping in and out of the pond. Every time a fly goes past, one of the frogs flicks out a tongue to catch it. Snap!

'It's a good life,' says Mum. 'Lots of sun. Plenty of flies. And all my family around me.'

The Frog family sit on their lily pads, watching for flies.

1) Fill in the missing words:

This story is about a f ___ ___ ___ ___ ___ of frogs.
The frogs sit in the s ___ ___ ___ ___ ___ ___ ___ all day.
The frogs c ___ ___ ___ ___ flies.
The noise they make is S ___ ___ ___ !

2) Look at the picture and read the caption. What do you think a lily pad is?

I think a lily pad is _____

3) What sound do the frogs make? How do you know? _____

_____

4) What does 'dipping in and out of the pond' mean? _____

_____

5) What do you think the frogs do with the flies?

I think _____

6) Why does Mum say it is a good life? _____

_____

Name _____

Frogs ahoy!

Here are the Frog family. Mum, Dad, Big Brother, Little Brother and Baby Sister. They love to spend the day sitting in the sunshine, dipping in and out of the pond. Every time a fly goes past, one of the frogs flicks out a tongue. Snap!

'It's a good life,' says Mum. 'Lots of sun. Plenty of flies. And all my family around me.'

'Mmmm,' says Dad. 'But I'm going down to the bottom of the pond to see what I can see.'

'Can I come with you?' asks Big Brother. 'I'm fed up with catching flies. I want to catch something else.'

'OK,' says Dad and they both dive off their lily pads into the deep pond.

The Frog family sit on their lily pads, watching for flies.

1) Who is this writing about? _____

2) Is it fiction or non-fiction? How can you tell? _____

_____

3) What does 'dipping' in and out of the pond mean? _____

_____

4) What do you think happens when the frogs flick out their tongues?

_____

5) Do you think Mum Frog is: Put a ✔

angry? ☐   happy? ☐   bored? ☐   sad? ☐

6) How do you know? _____

7) What is Big Brother Frog fed up with?

the pond? ☐   his family? ☐   sunbathing? ☐   catching flies? ☐

8) Why do Dad Frog and Big Brother Frog dive off their lily pads?

_____

_____

Name _____

Frogs ahoy!

Down at the pond there live a happy Frog family: Mum, Dad, Big Brother, Little Brother and Baby Sister. Most days the frogs sit on their lily pads, basking in the sunshine, waiting for passing flies. Every time a fly goes by, one of the frogs flicks out its tongue. Snap!

'It's a good life,' says Mum. 'Lots of sun. Plenty of flies. And all my family around me.'

'Mmmm,' says Dad. 'But I'm going down to the bottom of the pond to see what I can see.'

'Can I come with you?' asks Big Brother. 'I'm fed up with catching flies. I want to catch something else.'

'OK,' says Dad and they both dive off their lily pads into the deep pond.

ribbit,ribbit

ribbit,ribbit

ribbit,ribbit

The Frog family sit on their lily pads, watching for flies.

1) Who is this story about? _____

2) What kind of writing is this?   Put a ✔

   a recount ☐   information ☐   instructions ☐   fiction ☐

   How do you know?_____

3) The words say the frogs like 'basking in the sunshine'. Does this mean they like:

   arguing? ☐   croaking? ☐   sunbathing? ☐   jumping? ☐

4) Look at the words *a fly goes by* – what do you notice about them?

   They are in alphabetical order. ☐   They rhyme. ☐

   They should be in speech marks. ☐   They should be in capital letters. ☐

5) How do the frogs catch flies? _____

6) What makes Mum contented?

   the sunshine ☐   the flies ☐   her family ☐   all of these things? ☐

7) Who is not content? What do they do about it?

   _____

   _____

Name _____

The fantastic frog-jumping contest

The Frog children are ready for a frog-jumping contest. They are going to see which of them can jump the highest and the furthest.

Big Brother Frog is sure he will win. He thinks he is the best jumper. He puffs out his chest.

Little Brother Frog thinks he might lose. He hasn't had much practice.

Baby Frog doesn't know if she can jump at all.

The Frogs are going to jump one at a time. Big Brother first. Little Brother second. Baby Frog last.

Dad is at the start, ready to shout 'Go!'

Mum is at the other end, hoping that Baby Frog will jump right into her arms and win.

1) Fill in the missing words:

There is going to be a fantastic f ___ ___ ___ -jumping contest.

The three frogs are going to j ___ ___ ___ .

Big Brother is going to jump f ___ ___ ___ ___ .

Little Brother is going to jump s ___ ___ ___ ___ ___ .

Baby Frog will jump l ___ ___ ___ .

2) Why does Big Brother think he will win?

_____

3) How can you tell he is proud?

_____

4) In which order will the frogs jump?

_____

Name _____

The fantastic frog-jumping contest

The Frog children are ready for a frog-jumping contest. They are going to see which of them can jump the highest and the furthest.

Big Brother Frog is sure he will win. He thinks he is the best jumper. He puffs out his chest.

Little Brother Frog thinks he might lose. He hasn't had much practice.

Baby Frog doesn't know if she can jump at all.

The Frogs are going to jump one at a time. Big Brother first. Little Brother second. Baby Frog last.

Dad is at the start, ready to shout 'Go!'

Mum is at the other end, hoping that Baby Frog will jump right into her arms and win.

1) What is a contest? Put a ✔

   a race ☐   a game ☐   a competition ☐   a joke ☐

2) Which words tell you that Big Brother is proud of himself?

   _____

3) Why does Little Brother think he might lose? Is it because:

   he is smaller? ☐   his legs aren't so strong? ☐   he is tired? ☐

4) What does Baby Frog think?

   _____

5) Which words tell you that the frogs are not going to jump all at the same time?

   _____

6) Who will jump second?

   _____

7) Think of an end to the story. Write it on another sheet of paper.

Name _____

The fantastic frog-jumping contest

Here are the Frog family, lined up, ready for a fantastic frog-jumping contest. They are going to see which young frog can jump the highest and the furthest.

Big Brother Frog is sure he is going to win. He thinks he is the best jumper because he's got long legs and he is very strong. He puffs out his chest proudly.

Little Brother Frog thinks he might lose because he isn't so good at jumping. He hasn't had much practice.

Baby Frog feels very nervous because she doesn't know if she can jump at all.

The Frogs are going to jump one at a time. Big Brother first. Little Brother second. Baby Frog last. Dad will see how high they go. Mum will mark the distance.

Dad is at the start, ready to shout 'Go!'

Mum is at the other end, wishing with all her heart that Baby Frog could jump right into her arms and win.

1) What is the main idea of the story? _____

_____

2) What does 'lined up' mean? _____

3) Why does Big Brother frog puff out his chest? _____

4) Write three things that you know about Big Brother. _____

_____

5) Why does Little Brother think he will lose? Because:

he can't jump high? ☐   he can't jump far? ☐

he can't jump at all? ☐   he hasn't had much practice? ☐

6) Will the frogs jump   all together ☐   one by one ☐

7) Which words tell you this? _____

8) Who is going to start the contest? _____

9) Why do you think Mum is 'wishing with all her heart' that Baby Frog will win?

_____

Name _____

Poems

Read these poems with someone and listen to the words.

Creepy Crawlies

How would it be
If an ant came to tea
And a slug was invited to dinner?
And what about lunch
With a big hairy bunch
Of spiders, each waving a spinner?
And for supper your guests
Could be all sorts of pests
That you'd find in the oddest of
    places —
Earthworms and slugs,
Huge stag beetles and bugs —
All with big smiles on their faces!

Caterpillar

I'm a fat little grub,
Here am I, here am I,
Munching away at the leaves.
I'm a fat little grub,
Here am I, here am I,
And nobody else quite
    believes
That this fat little grub
That is I, that is I,
Will one day be
  — a butterfly!

Teddy Bear

Teddy bear
Is always there
Whether I'm good or bad.
Teddy bear
Is always there
Whether I'm happy or sad.
Teddy bear
Is always there
Ready for a cuddle
Ready for a hug
Ready to be tucked in bed,
Nice and snug.

Millipede

Don't try to race a millipede
Whatever else you do.
The millipede will always win —
It's got more legs than you!

Snails

Snails crawl around
With their homes on their backs,
And wherever they go
They leave silver tracks.

1) What are these poems mostly about? _____

2) The poem that is the odd one out is _____

3) Why is it the odd one out? _____

4) Do the poems rhyme? _____

5) Which poem do you like the best? _____

6) Why? _____

7) Collect some more poems and make them into a book.

Name _____

Poems

Read the poems with someone and listen to the words.

Creepy Crawlies

How would it be
If an ant came to tea
And a slug was invited to dinner?
And what about lunch
With a big hairy bunch
Of spiders, each waving a spinner?
And for supper your guests
Could be all sorts of pests
That you'd find in the oddest of
        places –
Earthworms and slugs,
Huge stag beetles and bugs –
All with big smiles on their faces!

Caterpillar

I'm a fat little grub,
Here am I, here am I,
Munching away at the
        leaves.
I'm a fat little grub,
Here am I, here am I,
And nobody else quite
        believes
That this fat little grub
That is I, that is I,
Will one day be
    – a butterfly!

Teddy Bear

Teddy bear
Is always there
Whether I'm good or bad.
Teddy bear
Is always there
Whether I'm happy or sad.
Teddy bear
Is always there
Ready for a cuddle
Ready for a hug
Ready to be tucked in bed,
Nice and snug.

Millipede

Don't try to race a millipede
Whatever else you do.
The millipede will always win –
It's got more legs than you!

Snails

Snails crawl around
With their homes on their backs,
And wherever they go
They leave silver tracks.

1) Would all the poems fit into the same set? _____

2) Why?_____

3) Which sets could you have? _____

4) Find words in the poems to rhyme with:

   I _____ backs _____ do _____ hug _____

5) Which poem do you like the best? _____

6) Why do you like it?_____

7) Find some more poems to fit into your sets.

Name _____

Poems

Read the poems with someone and listen to the words. The poems will fit into an anthology for your class. Will they all fit into the same set?

Creepy Crawlies

How would it be
If an ant came to tea
And a slug was invited to dinner?
And what about lunch
With a big hairy bunch
Of spiders, each waving a spinner?
And for supper your guests
Could be all sorts of pests
That you'd find in the oddest of places –
Earthworms and slugs,
Huge stag beetles and bugs –
All with big smiles on their faces!

Caterpillar

I'm a fat little grub,
Here am I, here am I,
Munching away at the
    leaves.
I'm a fat little grub,
Here am I, here am I,
And nobody else quite
    believes
That this fat little grub
That is I, that is I,
Will one day be
    – a butterfly!

Teddy Bear

Teddy bear
Is always there
Whether I'm good or bad.
Teddy bear
Is always there
Whether I'm happy or sad.
Teddy bear
Is always there
Ready for a cuddle
Ready for a hug
Ready to be tucked in bed,
Nice and snug.

Millipede

Don't try to race a millipede
Whatever else you do.
The millipede will always win –
It's got more legs than you!

Snails

Snails crawl around
With their homes on their backs,
And wherever they go
They leave silver tracks.

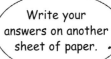
Write your answers on another sheet of paper.

1) The word 'anthology' is another word for:

   chapter ☐   collection ☐   publish ☐   poetry ☐

2) An anthology could have sets of poems or stories in it. What sets might these poems fit into?

3) The poems all rhyme in some way. Are the rhyming patterns all the same? ☐ different? ☐

4) What is another word for 'munching'? eating ☐ drinking ☐ stroking ☐ blowing ☐

5) In the Creepy Crawlies poem, what does it mean when it says 'waving a spinner'?

6) What do you think the 'milli' bit of millipede means? Do you know any more words that begin with 'milli'? Write them down. What do they mean?

7) Name four different minibeasts from the poems.

8) What is the teddy bear? another minibeast ☐ a mammal ☐ an insect ☐ a toy ☐

9) Which poem do you like best? Give a reason for your answer.

Name _____

Ryan Rabbit gets chickenpox

Ryan Rabbit did not feel well.

His head ached. He felt dizzy. He didn't want to go to school.

'You feel very hot,' his mum said. 'I think you'd better stay at home today.'

Ryan stayed in bed. By lunchtime he had three red spots on his face.

By teatime he had fifteen red spots on his tummy.

By bedtime, he was covered with spots.

'I think you have caught chickenpox,' said Mum. 'We'd better call the doctor.'

1) Fill in the missing words:

Ryan Rabbit did not feel w ___ ___ ___ .

Mum said Ryan was h ___ ___ .

Ryan did not go to sch ___ ___ ___ .

2) Where did the first spots appear? _____

_____

3) Mum said he must h ___ ___ ___ caught chickenpox.

4) Did all the spots come at the same time? _____

5) What did Ryan look like by bedtime? _____

_____

6) Have you ever been poorly like this? Tell or write about it.

Name _____

Ryan Rabbit gets chickenpox

Ryan Rabbit did not feel well.

His head ached. He felt dizzy. He didn't want to go to school.

'You feel very hot,' his mum said. 'I think you'd better stay at home today.'

Ryan stayed in bed. By lunchtime he had three red spots on his face.

By teatime he had fifteen red spots on his tummy.

By bedtime, he was covered with spots.

'I think you have caught chickenpox,' said Mum. 'We'd better call the doctor.'

1) Circle the correct answers:

Ryan Rabbit felt:	great	not well	ready to play
Ryan Rabbit had:	a sore finger	a cold	a headache

2) Why didn't Ryan go to school? _____

_____

3) Write how many spots Ryan had at lunchtime. _____

_____

4) How many spots did he have by teatime? _____

_____

5) What did his mum say he must have caught? _____

_____

6) What do you think 'chickenpox' is? _____

_____

7) Have you ever felt poorly like Ryan Rabbit? _____

8) Tell or write about when you were not well.

Name _____

Ryan Rabbit gets chickenpox

Ryan Rabbit did not feel well. His head ached. He felt dizzy. He didn't want to go to school.

'You feel very hot,' his mum said. 'I think you'd better stay at home today.'

Ryan stayed in bed. By lunchtime he had three red spots on his face.

By teatime he had fifteen red spots on his tummy.

By bedtime, he was covered with spots.

'I think you've caught chickenpox,' said Mum. 'We'd better call the doctor.'

When the doctor came he said, 'Yes, it is definitely chickenpox.' He told Mum that the spots would be very itchy but Ryan must try not to scratch them. He gave her some lotion to put on the spots to help.

1) Why didn't Ryan go to school? Because:

it was Saturday? ☐   it was a holiday? ☐

he wanted to play? ☐   he was ill? ☐

2) What did Mum say?

'You have to go to school.' ☐   'Hurry up and get ready!' ☐

'I feel dizzy.' ☐   'You feel very hot.' ☐

3) How did Mum know Ryan felt hot? Was it:

because he told her? ☐   because he was in bed? ☐

because she touched his forehead? ☐   because he had his pyjamas on? ☐

4) What did the doctor tell them about the spots?

They would go away. ☐   They would be fine. ☐

Ryan mustn't scratch them. ☐   They were measles. ☐

5) What happened between lunchtime and teatime? _____

_____

6) Have you had chickenpox? Write or tell the story.

Name _____

Rabbit plants some seeds

One day, Rabbit found ten little seeds by a bush. 'I wonder what will happen if I plant them,' he thought.

He planted them in a row.

Every day he watered the seeds. Soon, the plants began to grow. They grew taller and taller and taller.

Wasn't he pleased when he found that he had grown ten big, strong sunflowers!

1) Fill in the missing words:

Rabbit found ___ ___ ___ little seeds.

He decided to ___ ___ ___ ___ ___ them.

He planted them in a ___ ___ ___ .

He watered the seeds every ___ ___ ___ .

The plants grew very ___ ___ ___ ___ .

The plants grew into big, strong

___ ___ ___ ___ ___ ___ ___ ___ ___ ___.

2) What happened first? _____

3) Then what did Rabbit do? _____

4) Why do you think the seeds grew? _____

_____

5) How did Rabbit feel at the end? _____

Name _____

Rabbit plants some seeds

One day, Rabbit found ten little seeds by a bush. 'I wonder what will happen if I plant them,' he thought.

He decided he would plant them. He planted them all in a row.

Every day Rabbit made sure that he watered the seeds. Soon, the plants began to grow. They grew taller and taller and taller.

'I wonder what they can be,' he thought and he still kept watering them every day.

Wasn't he pleased when he found that he had grown ten big, strong sunflowers!

1) What did Rabbit find? _____

2) Why do you think Rabbit decided to plant the seeds? _____

_____

3) How do you know this? _____

4) How did Rabbit plant the seeds? Put a ✔

One on top of another ☐   In threes ☐   In a row ☐

5) What did Rabbit do next? _____

6) What happened to the seeds when Rabbit watered them? _____

_____

7) Do you think Rabbit was glad he had planted the seeds? _____

8) How do you know? _____

9) Make a list of all the things that happen in the story, in the right order. Begin with:

Rabbit finds the seeds. _____

_____

_____

Name _____

Rabbit plants some seeds

One day, when he was playing on the hillside, Rabbit found ten little seeds by a bush. He was curious. 'I wonder what would happen if I planted them,' he thought.

Rabbit decided to plant the seeds so that he could find out. He planted them in a row.

Every day he made sure that he watered the seeds. Soon, the plants began to grow. They grew taller and taller and taller.

'I wonder what they can be,' he thought and he still kept watering them every day.

Wasn't Rabbit surprised and pleased when he found that he had grown ten big, strong sunflowers!

1) What kind of writing is this? Put a ✔

   instructions ☐   a letter ☐   non-fiction ☐   a story ☐

2) How do you know this? _____

   _____

3) What does the text mean when it says Rabbit 'was curious'? _____

   _____

4) What was Rabbit thinking when the plants were growing? _____

   _____

5) What did Rabbit make sure to do? _____

6) Why do you think the plants grew? _____

   _____

7) Describe how Rabbit felt when he saw the sunflowers. _____

   _____

8) The story is about things that happen, one after another. What happened first?

   _____

9) On the back of this sheet, list all the things that happen in order that they happen. Use your list to write the story in your own words.

Name _____

How to make a snake

What you need:

plate

string or wool

scissors

thin card

pencil

crayons

What to do:

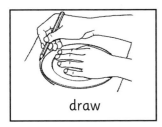
draw

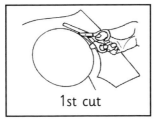
1st cut

draw a spiral

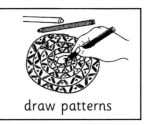
draw patterns

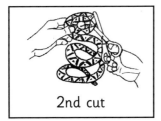
2nd cut

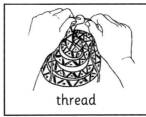
thread

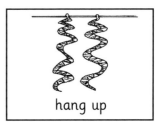
hang up

1) Fill in the missing words:

This page shows you how to m ___ ___ ___ a sn ___ ___ ___ .

These are the things that you need: A p ___ ___ ___ ___

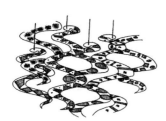

Some c ___ ___ ___

A pair of s ___ ___ ___ ___ ___ ___ ___

Some c ___ ___ ___ ___ ___ ___

A p ___ ___ ___ ___ ___

Some s t ___ ___ ___ ___ or w ___ ___ ___

2) What do you think you do first?

First, you _____

3) What do you do after you have drawn patterns on the snake?

_____

4) What is the last thing you do?

_____

5) Follow the instructions to make the snake.

Name _____

How to make a snake

What you need:

A plate

Scissors

Thin card

String or wool

Felt-tipped pens
or crayons

A pencil

What you do:

1) Draw round the plate.

2) Cut out the circle.

3) Draw a spiral inside the circle.

4) Draw patterns on the snake.

5) Cut along the spiral.

6) Thread string or wool through the snake's tail.

7) Display the snakes.

1) What kind of writing is this? Put a ✔

   a) a story ☐   b) information ☐

   c) a recipe ☐   d) instructions ☐

2) If you follow the instructions, what will be missing from the snake? Put a ✔

   a) its tail ☐   b) its tongue ☐

   c) its eyes ☐   d) its legs ☐

3) Which of the things you need could you use to make a tongue for the snake? How would you do it?

_____

_____

4) Why do you need to draw patterns on the snake?

_____

Remember to write in sentences.

5) What shape do you need to make a spiral?

   a square ☐   an oblong ☐   a circle ☐   a triangle ☐

6) Follow the instructions to make the snake.

Name _____

How to make a snake

You can make a display of paper snakes across your classroom. This is how you do it.

You will need:
- A plate
- A pencil
- A pair of scissors
- Some thin card to draw on
- Some felt-tipped pens or crayons to colour with
- Some string or wool to hang the snakes up with

This is what you do:
- First, you need to draw round the plate on the card, with the pencil, to make a circle.
- Next, you should cut out the circle carefully and draw a spiral inside it.
- When you have drawn a really good spiral that looks a bit like a curled up snake, draw some patterns on the snake. You could use an information book to find out what kinds of patterns snakes have or you could make up your own. Draw two eyes on the head end.
- Use the scissors to cut along the line of the spiral.
- Thread the string or wool through the tail of the snake. You could hang a line of snakes across your classroom to make a reptile house.

1) What kind of writing is this?   Put a ✔

a) fiction ☐   b) poetry ☐

c) a list ☐   d) instructions ☐

2) Why do you need thread or wool?   Put a ✔

a) To tie the snakes together. ☐

b) To make a tail on the snake. ☐

c) To hang each snake up. ☐

d) To make eyes on the snake. ☐

3) After following all of the instructions, something is missing from each snake. Is it: Put a ✔

a) teeth? ☐   b) a tongue? ☐

c) eyes? ☐   d) a tail? ☐

4) Which word tells you what kind of animal a snake is?   Put a ✔

a) spiral ☐   b) pattern ☐

c) reptile ☐   d) thread ☐

5) Where could you find real snakeskin patterns? _____

_____

6) On the back of this sheet, write the instructions as a numbered list, in the correct order.

7) Make some snakes.

Name _____

Making a list

A list shows a lot of things that go together. You can make lists of anything.

There are different kinds of lists. Some are in order. They might be in alphabetical order, time order or size order, like this:

Alphabetical	Time	Size
cartoon	Monday	mouse
castle	Tuesday	guinea pig
cat	Wednesday	rabbit

1) Write the labels for the pictures above. Use these words to help you:

skirt, trousers, swimming costume, coat, hat, scarf, boots, trainers

2) Write the missing words:

A list shows things that go t ___ ___ ___ ___ ___ ___ ___ .

You can have d ___ ___ ___ ___ ___ ___ ___ ___ kinds of lists.

These are in alphabetical order: cartoon, castle, ___ ___ ___ .

These are in time order: Monday, ___ ___ ___ ___ ___ ___ ___, Wednesday.

These are in ___ ___ ___ ___ order: mouse, guinea pig, rabbit.

3) If you put the words for the pictures above into a list, what heading would it have? Put a ✔

Games ☐   Things to do ☐   Shopping ☐   Clothes ☐

Name _____

Making a list

A list shows some things that go together. Lists are very useful. They help you to remember things. You can make lists of anything.

Some lists are in order. They might be in alphabetical order. They might be in time order. They might be in size order. Like this:

Alphabetical	Time	Size
cartoon	Monday	mouse
castle	Tuesday	guinea pig
cat	Wednesday	rabbit

1) Write the labels for the pictures above. Use these words to help you:

   skirt, trousers, swimming costume, coat, hat, scarf, boots, trainers

2) Which of these words could you add to that list?   Put a ✔

   shorts ☐   flowers ☐   sandals ☐   beachball ☐

3) The text says that lists are useful. Do you agree? Why?

   _____

4) If all the children in a class look after the class pet, how would a list help them?

   _____

5) Find the contents page in a book and have a look at the list. What order do you think it is in?

   alphabetical order ☐   size order ☐   page order ☐

Name _____

Making a list

A list shows some things that go together. They help you to remember things. You can make lists of anything – perhaps names, animals, shopping, toys.

Some lists are in order. They might be in alphabetical order. They might be in time order. They might be in size order. Like this:

List A	List B	List C
cartoon	Monday	mouse
castle	Tuesday	guinea pig
cat	Wednesday	rabbit

Lists are very useful. A list might show you what is in a cupboard, whose turn it is next or what you need to buy when you go shopping. You can have lists of things you want to do, things you have to do or things you want to save up for. You can make a list of who you want to invite to your birthday and a list of the party games to play.

1) Write the labels for the pictures above. Use these words to help you:

   skirt, trousers, swimming costume, coat, hat, scarf, boots, trainers

2) Looking at the lists above, which one is in alphabetical order? A, B, or C _____

   Which one is in size order? A, B, or C _____   Which one is in time order? A, B, or C _____

3) The text says that lists are useful. Do you agree? Why? _____

   _____

4) Why might you put a list up on a cupboard? _____

   _____

5) Choose one kind of list described in the text above. On the back of this sheet, give it a heading and put your own information into it.

Name _____

At the park

Sam is at the park with his dad. There is a very high climbing frame.

Dad says, 'Don't climb on that, Sam. It doesn't look very safe!'

But Sam loves climbing frames more than anything.

When his dad isn't looking, he starts to climb...

1) Finish these sentences:

Sam is at the p ___ ___ ___ .

Sam can see a climbing fr ___ ___ ___ .

Dad thinks the climbing frame is not s ___ ___ ___ .

2) What does Sam like best at the park?

_____

3) Which words tell you what the climbing frame is like?

_____

4) Why does Dad tell Sam not to climb on the frame?

_____

5) Does Sam:

do as he's told? ☐   listen to Dad's warning? ☐   ignore his dad? ☐

6) What do you think will happen? Why? _____

_____

7) Tell the story.

Name _____

At the park

Sam is at the park with his dad. There is a very high climbing frame.

Dad says, 'Don't climb on that, Sam. It doesn't look very safe!'

But Sam loves climbing frames more than anything.

When his dad isn't looking, he starts to climb...

1) Where are Sam and his dad?

_____

2) Circle the names of the equipment that is in this park:

swings   roundabout

see saw   climbing frame

3) Which words tell you what Sam likes best at the park?

_____

4) Which words describe the climbing frame?

_____

5) Why does Dad tell Sam not to climb on the climbing frame? Put a ✔

It is too high. ☐   It is rickety. ☐

It is wet and slippery. ☐   It doesn't look safe. ☐

6) Why do you think Sam waits till his dad isn't looking?

_____

7) What do you think will happen?

_____

8) Tell or write the story.

Name _____

At the park

Sam is at the park with his dad. There are swings and a see-saw. There is a very high climbing frame. Dad says, 'Don't climb on that, Sam. It doesn't look very safe!'

But Sam loves climbing frames more than anything.

When his dad isn't looking, he starts to climb.

Sam goes higher and higher and higher. He goes through the spaces and across the bridges.

He keeps on going until, all of a sudden, the wood that he is holding onto begins to wobble...

1) Where are Sam and his dad?

_____

2) Why does Dad say, 'Don't climb on that'?

_____

3) What do the words 'It doesn't look very safe,' tell you?   Put a ✔

The climbing frame is high. ☐   What Sam is doing looks dangerous. ☐

The climbing frame might be dangerous. ☐   Sam is not very good at climbing. ☐

4) Sam waits till his dad isn't looking. Then what does he do?

_____

5) Match the words to make sentences that tell what Sam does on the climbing frame.

Sam goes	through the spaces.
He goes	begins to wobble.
The wood he is holding onto	higher and higher and higher.

6) What do you think will happen? Why do you think this?

_____

_____

7) Tell or write the end of the story.

Name _____

Mrs Rabbit's family

Mrs Rabbit

Brown Rabbit

Blue Rabbit

Grey Rabbit

Pink Rabbit

1) Fill in the missing names. Use the picture to help you.

This is

Mrs R __ __ __ __ __

and her family.

These are the names of her children:

B __ __ __ __ Rabbit

P __ __ __ Rabbit

B __ __ __ Rabbit

G __ __ __ Rabbit

2) After Mrs Rabbit, which rabbit is the biggest? Put a ✔

Yellow Rabbit ☐   Green Rabbit ☐

Brown Rabbit ☐   Red Rabbit ☐

3) Which two rabbits do you think are twins? Why do you think this?

I think _____

are twins because _____

4) Is Pink Rabbit bigger or smaller than the twins?

Pink Rabbit is _____

5) How many children does Mrs Rabbit have?

one ☐   two ☐   three ☐   four ☐

Name _____

Mrs Rabbit's family

Mrs Rabbit is a very friendly rabbit.

She lives in a hole under a tree.

Mrs Rabbit has four children. They are Brown Rabbit, Pink Rabbit, Blue Rabbit and Grey Rabbit.

Blue Rabbit and Grey Rabbit are the smallest. They are twins.

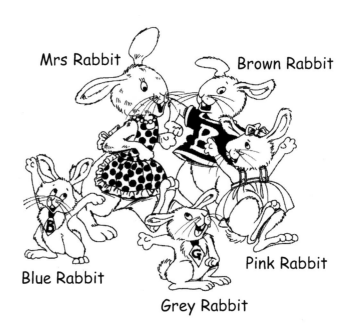

Mrs Rabbit   Brown Rabbit

Blue Rabbit

Grey Rabbit

Pink Rabbit

1) This writing is part of a story. What do you think it is telling you?   Put a ✔

  a) What happens. ☐   b) How the story ends. ☐

  c) Who the characters are. ☐   d) When the story happens. ☐

2) How many children does Mrs Rabbit have?   Put a ✔

  a) six ☐   b) ten ☐   c) seven ☐   d) four ☐

3) Where do the Rabbit family live?

The Rabbit family live _____

4) Write the names of Mrs Rabbit's children, starting with the biggest and ending with the smallest.

5) Which rabbits are twins? Put a ✔

Brown and Pink ☐   Brown and Blue ☐

Grey and Pink ☐   Blue and Grey ☐

6) On the back of this sheet, write a sentence to describe Brown Rabbit.

Name _____

Mrs Rabbit's family

Mrs Rabbit is a very friendly rabbit. She lives in a hole under a tree. Mrs Rabbit has four children. They are Brown Rabbit, Pink Rabbit, Blue Rabbit and Grey Rabbit.

Brown Rabbit is the tallest, except for Mrs Rabbit. Blue Rabbit and Grey Rabbit are the smallest. They are twins.

The rabbits love playing in the fields. They go hopping and jumping across the grass. Brown Rabbit can hop higher than any of the others. Pink Rabbit likes to hide amongst the toadstools. Blue Rabbit and Grey Rabbit have lots of fun playing Tig Off Ground.

1) What kind of writing is this the beginning of?   Put a ✔

   a) informational writing ☐   b) a story ☐

   c) instructions ☐   d) a poem ☐

2) Who are the Rabbit family?

   a) the authors ☐   b) the readers ☐

   c) characters in the story ☐   d) the illustrators ☐

3) Which words tell you what Brown Rabbit is good at?   Put a ✔

   a) go hopping and jumping ☐   b) can hop higher ☐

   c) love playing in the fields ☐   d) a very friendly rabbit ☐

4) What does Pink Rabbit like to do? _____

_____

5) What is Blue Rabbit and Grey Rabbit's favourite game? _____

6) Which rabbit is which? Write the name of each rabbit in the box by their picture.

7) Using the text to help you, write two sentences that tell something about Brown Rabbit.

_____

_____

_____

Name _____

Butterflies

This diagram shows you how butterflies change from egg to adult.

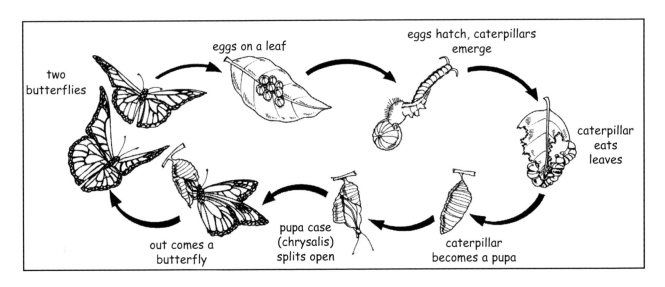

two butterflies

eggs on a leaf

eggs hatch, caterpillars emerge

caterpillar eats leaves

out comes a butterfly

pupa case (chrysalis) splits open

caterpillar becomes a pupa

Special words: eggs, leaf, leaves, caterpillar, hatch, pupa, chrysalis, butterfly

1) Fill in the missing words:

The female butterfly lays ___ ___ ___ ___ .

The eggs are on a ___ ___ ___ ___ .

Out of each egg comes a ___ ___ ___ ___ ___ ___ ___ ___ ___ ___ ___ .

The caterpillar eats the ___ ___ ___ ___ ___ ___ .

The caterpillar changes into a ___ ___ ___ ___ .

Out of the chrysalis comes a ___ ___ ___ ___ ___ ___ ___ ___ ___ .

2) Which of the special words means a small creature that crawls on leaves and eats them?

leaf ☐   hatch ☐   caterpillar ☐   butterfly ☐

3) This text is:

a picture ☐   a poem ☐   a story ☐   a diagram ☐

Name _____

Butterflies

This diagram shows you how butterflies change from egg to adult.

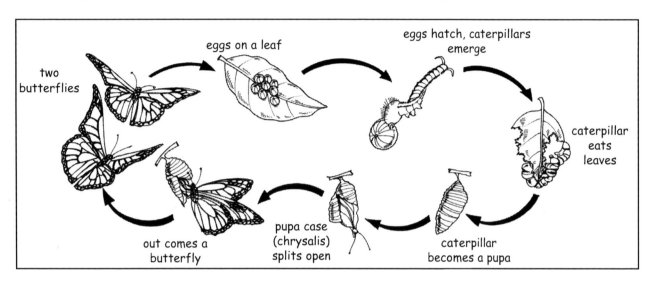

eggs on a leaf

eggs hatch, caterpillars emerge

two butterflies

caterpillar eats leaves

out comes a butterfly

pupa case (chrysalis) splits open

caterpillar becomes a pupa

1) What kind of writing is this?　　Put a ✔

   a poem ☐   instructions ☐   a diagram ☐   a story ☐

2) Which insect lays the eggs? _____

3) Which words tell you what come out of the eggs? _____

4) What do caterpillars eat? Do they eat:

   grubs ☐   flowers ☐   leaves ☐   eggs ☐

5) What is the word for what the caterpillar becomes before it is a butterfly?

   puppy ☐   puppet ☐   pupa ☐   pupil ☐

6) The case the pupa is in is called a:

   crystal ☐   chrysanthemum ☐   crick ☐   chrysalis ☐

7) Which words tell you what happens to the chrysalis?

   breaks apart ☐   splits open ☐   caterpillars emerge ☐

8) What comes out of the chrysalis? _____

9) Do you think this diagram shows you very clearly how a butterfly changes? Why do you think this?

_____

_____

Name _____

Butterflies

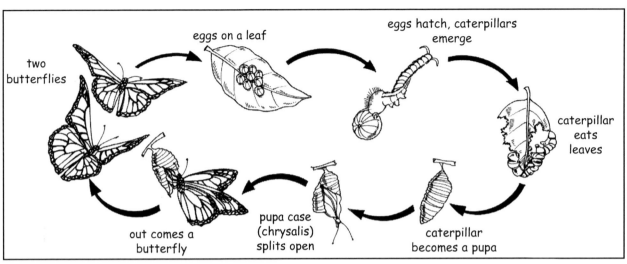

1) This diagram is called a 'flow diagram' or a 'cycle diagram'. Why do you think this is?

   _____

2) Is it a good way to give information? Give a reason for your answer.

   _____

3) Write three things you know about a caterpillar from reading the captions on the diagram.

   _____

   _____

   _____

4) Where does the butterfly come from?

   Out of the egg ☐   Out of the caterpillar ☐   Out of the chrysalis ☐

5) Which words tell you that the chrysalis breaks?

   _____

6) What happens after the butterflies have emerged?

   They die ☐   They fly off ☐   They eat the caterpillars ☐

   The cycle starts again when they lay eggs ☐

7) Using the diagram and the captions, write a short description of how butterflies change from egg to adult.

   _____

   _____

   _____ *Continue on the back of this sheet.*

Name _____

An index

INDEX

ant, 8, 17
beetle, 4, 15, 27
centipede, 2, 16, 23
dragonfly, 2, 13, 29
duck, 6, 7, 12
frog, 9, 11, 20, 24
grebe, 18, 22
ladybird, 5, 10
millipede, 3, 19, 23
stickleback, 14, 21, 24
water boatman, 24, 26, 28
water flea, 25
woodlouse, 25

30

An index page has a list of words. It is usually at the back of a book. It shows you where to find information. This index page is from a reference book about wildlife. The names of the creatures are in alphabetical order. The numbers show you on which page, or pages, you can find information about them.

1) Fill in the missing words:

You can find the duck on pages ___ , ___ and ___ ___.

The ___ ___ ___ ___ is in the book four times.

The woodlouse and the water flea are both on ___ ___ ___ ___ 25.

The stickleback is on pages 14, 21 and ___ ___.

2) How is an index page arranged?

_____

3) If you wanted to look up information about the water boatman, which pages would you turn to?

_____

4) Where could you find out about the grebe?

_____

5) What is this reference book all about?

_____

Name _____

An index

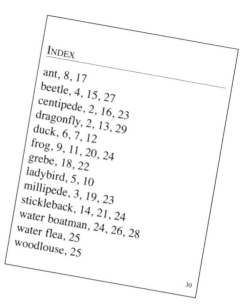

INDEX

ant, 8, 17
beetle, 4, 15, 27
centipede, 2, 16, 23
dragonfly, 2, 13, 29
duck, 6, 7, 12
frog, 9, 11, 20, 24
grebe, 18, 22
ladybird, 5, 10
millipede, 3, 19, 23
stickleback, 14, 21, 24
water boatman, 24, 26, 28
water flea, 25
woodlouse, 25

30

An index page has a list of words. It is usually at the back of a book. It shows you where to find information. This index page is from a reference book about wildlife. The names of the creatures are in alphabetical order. The numbers show you on which page, or pages, you can find information about them.

1) What is this reference book about?

   _____

2) What does an index page tell you?

   _____

3) Why do you think the names of the creatures are in alphabetical order? Because:

   that is the order they are in the book. ☐   it is the way they live at the pond. ☐

   It Is easy to find the creature you want. ☐   it Is the order they are born in. ☐

4) On which pages would you find information about a dragonfly? _____

   _____

5) Which creature appears on four different pages?

   _____

6) Which creature can you find on page 12?

   centipede ☐   grebe ☐   water boatman ☐   duck ☐

7) On the back of this sheet write about why you think an index page is important in a reference book.

Name _____

An index

INDEX

ant, 8, 17
beetle, 4, 15, 27
centipede, 2, 16, 23
dragonfly, 2, 13, 29
duck, 6, 7, 12
frog, 9, 11, 20, 24
grebe, 18, 22
ladybird, 5, 10
millipede, 3, 19, 23
stickleback, 14, 21, 24
water boatman, 24, 26, 28
water flea, 25
woodlouse, 25

30

1) Explain, in your own words, what an index is. _____

_____

2) What do you need the page numbers for? Put a ✔

To check the spelling. ☐

To find information. ☐

To learn the alphabet. ☐

3) Why do you think the list of words is in alphabetical order? Put a ✔

To make them easy to spell. ☐

To make them easy to find. ☐

To make the page look right. ☐

4) How many creatures are in the book? _____

5) Which creature appears on the most pages? _____

6) Which pages is the water boatman on? _____

7) Which creature can you find on pages 3, 19 and 23? _____

8) If you had to put the following in the index, where would you put them?

tadpole _____

kingfisher _____

cranefly _____

9) Find a reference book with an index and check that the index works like this.

Name _____

Frogs on a visit

One day, the Frog family were getting ready to go on a trip. Dad said, 'We will go to Next Pond. It will be good to see our friends.'

First, they had to go across a field. Hop, hop, hop they all went, through the grass.

Next, they had to go across a busy road. Leap, leap, leap they all went, across the road.

Soon they could see Next Pond. Jump, jump, jump they all went, to the edge of the pond.

Everyone was so excited to see them!

1) Fill in the missing words:

This is a story about the ___ ___ ___ ___ family.

They were going on a ___ ___ ___ ___.

They were going to Next ___ ___ ___ ___.

They hopped across a ___ ___ ___ ___ ___.

They leapt across a ___ ___ ___ ___.

They jumped to the ___ ___ ___ ___ of Next Pond.

2) What reason did Dad give for going?

_____

3) How did the journey end?

_____

4) Practise telling this story to someone.

_____

Name _____

Frogs on a visit

One day, the Frog family were getting ready to go on a trip. Dad said, 'We will go to Next Pond. It will be good to see our friends.'

First, they had to go across a field. Hop, hop, hop they all went, through the grass.

Next, they had to go across a busy road. Leap, leap, leap they all went, across the road.

Soon they could see Next Pond. Jump, jump, jump they all went, to the edge of the pond.

Everyone was so excited to see them!

1) What did the frogs go on?

   a picnic ☐   a holiday ☐   a walk ☐   a trip ☐

2) What did Dad say to his family? _____

   _____

3) Which words tell you why Dad wanted to go to Next Pond?

   _____

4) What did the frogs have to cross first? _____

5) How did they go? _____

6) What did the frogs have to cross second? _____

7) How did they go? _____

8) Why did they go jump, jump, jump? _____

9) Practise telling this story. Check you haven't missed anything out. Make it into a little book with pictures.

Name _____

Frogs on a visit

One day, the Frog family were getting ready to go on a trip. Dad said, 'We will go to Next Pond. It will be good to see our friends.'

The frogs all cheered.

Off they went. First, they had to go across a field. Hop, hop, hop they all went, through the grass.

Next, they had to go across a busy road. 'Make sure you keep safe,' said Dad. Leap, leap, leap they all went, across the road.

When everyone was on the other side, the frogs all cheered.

Soon they could see Next Pond. 'Not far now,' said Dad.

The frogs all cheered.

Jump, jump, jump they all went, to the edge of the pond.

Everyone was so excited to see them!

1) What is the main idea of this story?

Keeping safe. ☐   Going on a trip. ☐   Cheering. ☐   Going for a walk. ☐

2) Dad has three lots of dialogue in the story. What are they? _____

_____

_____

3) The frogs all cheered three times. When did they cheer? _____

_____

_____

4) The frogs moved in three different ways. Which ways? _____

_____

5) What did the frogs cross first? How did they cross? _____

_____

6) Why did Dad tell the frogs to make sure they kept safe when they went across the road?

_____

7) Was there anybody at Next Pond when the frogs arrived? How do you know? _____

_____

8) Practise telling this story. Make notes to remind yourself of everything that's in the story so that you get it in the right order. Make sure you have what Dad says in your story.

Name _____

Story book blurbs

1) Here are four story books. Read their titles and their blurbs.

2) Fill in the missing words:

___ ___ ___ goes on holiday   Rainy day at ___ ___ ___ ___ Pond

The great dinosaur ___ ___ ___ ___ ___ ___   Millie gets ___ ___ ___ ___

3) These stories are all about:

rainy days ☐   animals ☐   getting lost ☐   going on holiday ☐

4) What is the blurb for the story about the cat?

_____

_____

5) What is the title of the story about the frogs?

_____

6) What kind of story is the dinosaur story?

a fairy story ☐   an adventure story ☐   a folk tale

7) Talk about the four stories. What do you think will happen in them?

Name _____

Story book blurbs

1) Where does Cat go to stay? Why? _____

_____

2) What happens to the puppy?

_____

3) What is the title of the story about the frogs?

_____

4) What is the blurb about the dinosaur story?

_____

_____

5) Which story is an adventure story?

_____

6) Which story has a mystery in it?

_____

7) What is the same about all of these stories?

_____

8) Talk about what you think might happen in each story. Write one of your own. Make a little book about it.

Name _____

Story book blurbs

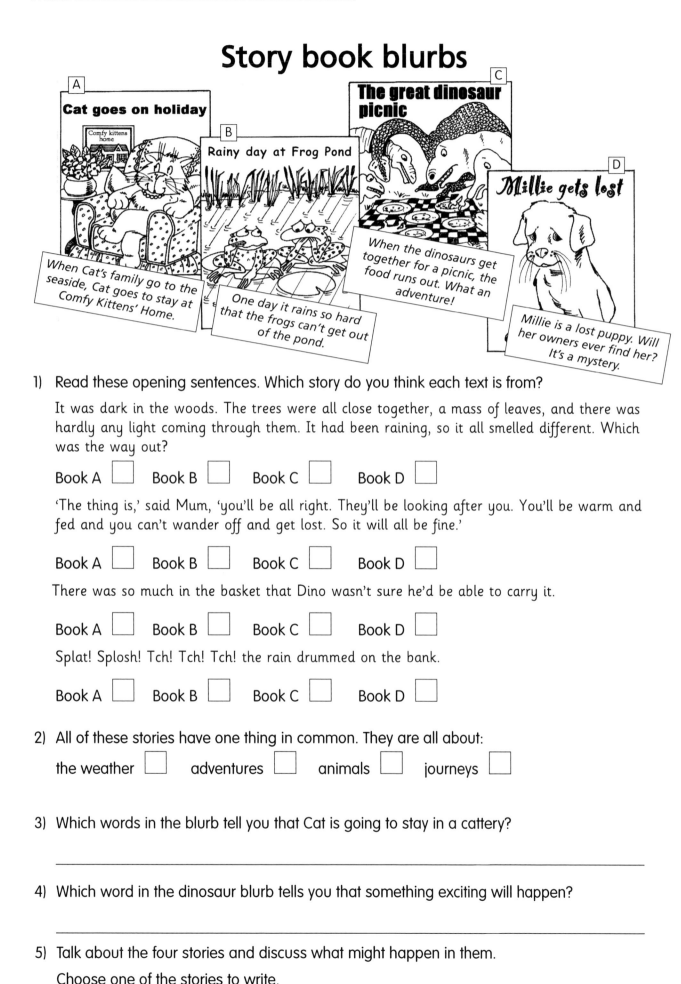

A — **Cat goes on holiday**
When Cat's family go to the seaside, Cat goes to stay at Comfy Kittens' Home.

B — **Rainy day at Frog Pond**
One day it rains so hard that the frogs can't get out of the pond.

C — **The great dinosaur picnic**
When the dinosaurs get together for a picnic, the food runs out. What an adventure!

D — **Millie gets lost**
Millie is a lost puppy. Will her owners ever find her? It's a mystery.

1) Read these opening sentences. Which story do you think each text is from?

It was dark in the woods. The trees were all close together, a mass of leaves, and there was hardly any light coming through them. It had been raining, so it all smelled different. Which was the way out?

Book A ☐   Book B ☐   Book C ☐   Book D ☐

'The thing is,' said Mum, 'you'll be all right. They'll be looking after you. You'll be warm and fed and you can't wander off and get lost. So it will all be fine.'

Book A ☐   Book B ☐   Book C ☐   Book D ☐

There was so much in the basket that Dino wasn't sure he'd be able to carry it.

Book A ☐   Book B ☐   Book C ☐   Book D ☐

Splat! Splosh! Tch! Tch! Tch! the rain drummed on the bank.

Book A ☐   Book B ☐   Book C ☐   Book D ☐

2) All of these stories have one thing in common. They are all about:

the weather ☐   adventures ☐   animals ☐   journeys ☐

3) Which words in the blurb tell you that Cat is going to stay in a cattery?

_____

4) Which word in the dinosaur blurb tells you that something exciting will happen?

_____

5) Talk about the four stories and discuss what might happen in them.
Choose one of the stories to write.

Name _____

The pond

The Frog family lives happily at Home Pond. The pond is just a hop across the farmer's field, then over a bridge and down a short path. It is just a small pond, with a steep bank all around it. Wild flowers and bushes grow at the edge.

1) Fill in the missing words:

The Frog Family lives at Home ___ ___ ___ ___ .

The pond is across the farmer's ___ ___ ___ ___ ___ .

To get there you need to go ___ ___ ___ ___ a bridge.

Then you go down a short ___ ___ ___ ___ .

2) Do you think the frogs like living at Home Pond? Yes ☐ No ☐

3) Which word tells you this? _____

4) How would you get to the pond?

Skip across a road? ☐ Hop across a farmer's field? ☐

5) Where do the wild flowers grow? _____

6) Draw a wild flower.

7) Do you think the pond is a good setting for a story about frogs? Yes ☐ No ☐

Name _____

The pond

The Frog family live happily at Home Pond. The pond is just a hop across the farmer's field, then over a bridge and down a short path. It is just a small pond, with a steep bank all around it. Wild flowers and bushes grow at the edge. Mum Frog thinks there could not be a prettier place to live in the whole, wide world.

1) What is Home Pond?

Where the farmer goes fishing? ☐ Where the boats sail? ☐

Where the Frog family live? ☐ Where big trees grow? ☐

2) Which phrase tells you that the Frog family like living at Home Pond?

_____

3) How would you get to Home Pond from the farmer's house?

_____

4) Is the steep bank:

where the frogs get money? ☐ a sharp slope? ☐

5) What grows around the edge of the pond? _____

6) Does Mum like Home Pond because it is:

the biggest place in the whole world? ☐ the friendliest place in the whole world? ☐

the prettiest place in the whole world? ☐ the nearest place in the whole world? ☐

7) Do you think that Home Pond is a good setting for a story about frogs? Why?

_____

8) Think of a different story that Home Pond might be a good setting for. Then say why.

A day in school ☐ A day at the theme park ☐ A day trip to the country ☐

_____

Name _____

The pond

The Frog Family live happily at Home Pond. The pond is just a hop across the farmer's field, then over a bridge and down a short path. It is just a small pond, with a steep bank all around it. Wild flowers and bushes grow at the edge. Mum Frog thinks there could not be a prettier place to live in the whole, wide world. 'It is as pretty as a picture here,' she says.

1) This is the beginning of a story. What does it tell you about? Put a ✔

The characters ☐   The farmer ☐   What happens ☐   The setting ☐

2) The words say Home Pond is just a hop across the farmer's field. Does it say this because:

you have to hop all the way? ☐   the farmer always hops? ☐

it is only 15cm away? ☐   the story is about frogs and frogs hop? ☐

3) Which of these phrases tells you best what the steep bank is?

a big hill ☐   a slippery slope ☐   a muddy ditch ☐   a sharp slope ☐

4) Which of these phrases tells you what Mum Frog thinks of where they live?

over a bridge ☐   grow at the edge ☐

the whole wide world ☐   as pretty as a picture ☐

5) Describe the setting of this story to someone, using as many words as you can remember from the text.

6) Do you think Mum Frog likes Home Pond? Write how you know this.

_____

_____

7) Use this setting as the beginning of a story of your own. Tell it or write it on another piece of paper.

Name _____

Fred Farley, famous author

This is the blurb for Fred Farley's new book.

Fred Farley, the famous author, lives at Home Farm with his family. Home Pond is on this land and Fred writes all his stories about the creatures who visit the pond. The first book he wrote is called 'Too Many Ducks'. Everyone loves Fred's books. His new story is called 'Dragonfly Dreams'.

1) Write the missing words:

Fred Farley, the famous ___ ___ ___ ___ ___ ___.

Fred writes ___ ___ ___ ___ ___ ___ ___.

The first book Fred wrote is called Too Many ___ ___ ___ ___ ___.

Fred's ___ ___ ___ story is called Dragonfly Dreams.

2) What does Fred write all his books about?

_____

3) What do other people think of Fred's books?

_____

4) What do you think Dragonfly Dreams might be about?

_____

5) Find a blurb about an author in one of your story books.

Name _____

Fred Farley, famous author

This is the blurb for Fred Farley's new book.

> Fred Farley, the famous author, lives at Home Farm with his family. Home Pond is on this land and Fred writes all his stories about the creatures who visit the pond. The first book he wrote is called 'Too Many Ducks'. Fred loves writing. He wanted to be a writer even when he was just a boy. Everyone loves Fred's books. His latest story is called 'Dragonfly Dreams' and Fred thinks it is the best story he has ever written.

1) What is an author?

Someone who lives in a pond. ☐   A frog. ☐

Someone who writes stories and books. ☐   A farmer . ☐

2) Which words tell you what Fred writes about? _____

_____

3) What was Fred's first book called?

At Home Pond ☐   Too Many Ducks ☐   Pond Visitors ☐

4) Why does Fred keep writing books?

_____

5) What does 'latest story' mean?

Dragonfly Dreams. ☐   The one Fred has just written. ☐

The best story ever. ☐   The story was too late to get published. ☐

6) Which would be another good title for a Fred Farley book? Say why.

Tiger's Train Trip ☐   The Castle Adventure ☐   Pondskater's Puzzle ☐

_____

7) Find some blurbs about authors in some of your own books and read them.

Name _____

Fred Farley, famous author

Fred Farley, the famous author, lives at Home Farm with his family. Home Pond is on this land and Fred writes all his stories about the creatures who visit the pond. He is as busy as a bee, writing all day long. The first book he wrote is called 'Too Many Ducks'. Fred loves writing. He wanted to be a writer even when he was just a boy. Everyone loves Fred's books. His latest story is called 'Dragonfly Dreams' and Fred thinks it is the best story he has ever written.

1) Is the text above: instructions? ☐   a blurb? ☐   a play? ☐

2) What is the text telling you about?

_____

3) Write three things you know about Fred Farley from the text.

_____

_____

_____

4) What does Fred write about?

_____

5) When did Fred first know he wanted to be a writer?

_____

6) There is a simile in the text. What is it? _____

7) What does the author think of Dragonfly Dreams?

_____

8) What does 'latest story' mean?

_____

9) Find some authors' blurbs in some of your books and compare them with Fred's.

Name _____

In space

In space
  maybe there's
  a new world
  and the people
  are green
  with three heads
  four eyes and
  a bucket
  on the end
  of their nose.
In space
  maybe there's a
  new world
  and the land is
  sticky like
  marmalade
  and the sea
  is red like
  stop on the
  traffic
  lights and
  the sun beats
  up instead of
  down and the
  wind chuckles
  instead of
  sighs and the
  rain's made of
  tears. In space
  maybe there's a
  new world
  and the daisies
  smell of new
  shoes and
  cornflakes taste like
  a day at the seaside
  and the fish fly and
  the birds swim and the
  elephants sing and
  the zebras dance and
  the monkeys go to
  school and
  the children have
  nothing to do but play
  in the trees
  all day.

©Irene Yates

1) Listen to the poem and read it where you can.

2) Which bits make you laugh? Try to remember the words of these parts.

3) What does 'the land is sticky like marmalade' mean? How could you describe it?

_____

_____

4) What does the poet mean when she says 'the rain's made of tears'? She means:

the sky is like the sea ☐

the sky is crying ☐

the sun dries up the rain ☐

the clouds burst ☐

5) Think about fish flying, elephants singing, zebras dancing and monkeys going to school. Would this be fun? Why?

_____

_____

6) Draw a picture of the part of the poem you like best.

Name _____

In space

In space
  maybe there's
  a new world
  and the people
  are green
  with three heads
  four eyes and
  a bucket
  on the end
  of their nose.
In space
  maybe there's a
  new world
  and the land is
  sticky like
  marmalade
  and the sea
  is red like
  stop on the
  traffic
  lights and
  the sun beats
  up instead of
  down and the
  wind chuckles
  instead of
  sighs and the
  rain's made of
  tears. In space
  maybe there's a
  new world
  and the daisies
  smell of new
  shoes and
  cornflakes taste like
  a day at the seaside
  and the fish fly and
  the birds swim and the
  elephants sing and
  the zebras dance and
  the monkeys go to
  school and
  the children have
  nothing to do but play
  in the trees
  all day.

©Irene Yates

1) Listen to the poem and read it.

2) Which words and phrases stay in your memory the most?

_____

_____

_____

3) Why do you think this is?

_____

_____

_____

4) Which bits of the poem make you laugh?

_____

_____

_____

5) Finish these words in a different way of your own:

The land is sticky like _____

_____

The sea is red like _____

_____

6) What do you think the writer means by the words 'a new world'?

_____

_____

7) Choose some of the ideas from this poem to help you write a poem of your own.

Name _____

In space

In space
  maybe there's
  a new world
  and the people
  are green
  with three heads
  four eyes and
  a bucket
  on the end
  of their nose.
In space
  maybe there's a
  new world
  and the land is
  sticky like
  marmalade
  and the sea
  is red like
  stop on the
  traffic
  lights and
  the sun beats
  up instead of
  down and the
  wind chuckles
  instead of
  sighs and the
  rain's made of
  tears. In space
    maybe there's a
  new world
  and the daisies
  smell of new
  shoes and
  cornflakes taste like
    a day at the seaside
  and the fish fly and
  the birds swim and the
  elephants sing and
    the zebras dance and
      the monkeys go to
  school and
      the children have
  nothing to do but play
    in the trees
      all day.

©Irene Yates

Listen to the poem and read it out loud to yourself.

This poem is meant to make you laugh. It is full of images.

An image is a group of words that put pictures into your head. Sometimes images are similes and sometimes they are metaphors.

1) There are three similes in the poem. (Remember, a simile uses the word 'like' or the word 'as'.) Write them here:

_____

_____

_____

2) Read it aloud to yourself. It is meant to make you laugh. It is full of words that put pictures into your head.

Make up words of your own to give different pictures, for:

The sea is red like...   The rain's made of...
The daisies smell of...   Cornflakes taste like...

3) Why do you think the poet lets the words start at different places along the lines?

_____

4) What is imaginative about the words 'the fish fly and the birds swim and the elephants sing and the zebras dance'?

_____

5) Which images do you find the funniest? Write them here and say why they are funny.

_____

_____

_____

6) Talk about the images in the poem and make up some of your own. Write them on another sheet of paper.

7) Write a poem of your own, beginning with:

  In space
    maybe there's a
    new world
    and the people...

Name _____

In the park

There's a park down by us with a climbing frame
That's shaped like a ship on the sea.
It's got wooden sails and a rig at the side
And an anchor you can't quite pull free.
You can climb up a mast to reach the crow's-nest
And see right across to our town;
And when you jump off or walk 'cross the plank
You can act like you're going to drown.
If you're on the wheel you can tell all the others
Exactly what they have to do
For everyone knows you're the captain
And they are the cowardly crew.
The climbing frame shaped like a ship on the sea
Is not really just what it seems –
For it makes Treasure Island feel real in your head,
And pirates appear in your dreams.

© Irene Yates

1) Fill in the missing words:

The poem is about a climbing frame at the ___ ___ ___ ___.

The climbing frame is shaped like a ___ ___ ___ ___.

The ship has wooden ___ ___ ___ ___ ___.

You can climb up the ___ ___ ___ ___.

From the top you can see across to the ___ ___ ___ ___.

2) What do children play at when they are on the climbing frame? Put a ✔

football ☐   ships at sea ☐   snakes and ladders ☐   tig off ground ☐

3) Is the climbing frame good for pretend games? How do you know?

_____

4) How does the climbing frame shaped like a ship make the children feel when they play on it?

_____

5) If you were pretending to be the captain which bit of the ship would you be playing on? Write the answer on the back of this sheet.

Name _____

In the park

There's a park down by us with a climbing frame
That's shaped like a ship on the sea.
It's got wooden sails and a rig at the side
And an anchor you can't quite pull free.
You can climb up a mast to reach the crow's-nest
And see right across to our town;
And when you jump off or walk 'cross the plank
You can act like you're going to drown.
If you're on the wheel you can tell all the others
Exactly what they have to do
For everyone knows you're the captain
And they are the cowardly crew.
The climbing frame shaped like a ship on the sea
Is not really just what it seems —
For it makes Treasure Island feel real in your head,
And pirates appear in your dreams.

© Irene Yates

1) What is this poem about?

pirates at sea ☐   a climbing frame in the park ☐   dreaming ☐   sailing ☐

2) The poem says:

You can climb up a mast to reach the crow's-nest
And see right across to our town;

Do you think the 'crow's-nest' is:

the deck ☐   the highest part of the climbing frame ☐   the plank ☐

3) What do you think 'an anchor you can't quite pull free' is?

_____

4) Where do you have to be to see right across to the town?

_____

5) The poet uses the words below. What do you think this means?

And when you jump off or walk 'cross the plank
You can act like you're going to drown.

_____

_____

Name _____

In the park

There's a park down by us with a climbing frame
That's shaped like a ship on the sea.
It's got wooden sails and a rig at the side
And an anchor you can't quite pull free.
You can climb up a mast to reach the crow's-nest
And see right across to our town;
And when you jump off or walk 'cross the plank
You can act like you're going to drown.
If you're on the wheel you can tell all the others
Exactly what they have to do
For everyone knows you're the captain
And they are the cowardly crew.
The climbing frame shaped like a ship on the sea
Is not really just what it seems —
For it makes Treasure Island feel real in your head,
And pirates appear in your dreams.

© Irene Yates

1) What is this poem about?

_____

2) What is shaped like a ship on the sea?_____

3) What are the sails made from?_____

4) What do you think the crow's-nest is? Why? _____

_____

5) Write three things that children pretend when they are on the ship.

_____

_____

6) What do you have to do to be captain? _____

7) What does the poet mean when she says:

   The climbing frame shaped like a ship on the sea
   Is not really just what it seems

_____

_____

8) Read the poem again, very carefully. Choose your favourite parts and write them into a story or poem of your own.

Name _____

The fox and the goat

Once there was a fox who drank water from a well.

One day he leaned over so far to get the water that he fell in. The wall of the well was too high for him to get out again.

Along came a goat. 'Why are you down in the well?' he asked the fox.

'The water is so nice,' said the fox. 'Why don't you jump down and taste it?'

The goat jumped into the well. As soon as he got to the bottom, the fox jumped on his back and climbed out.

'Ha, ha, ha,' laughed the fox. 'You should look before you leap, friend goat!' And off he ran.

1) Fill in the missing words:

   The fox drank water from the ___ ___ ___ ___.

   The fox could ___ ___ ___ get out.

   Along came a ___ ___ ___ ___.

2) Why did the fox lean out too far?

   _____

3) Who tumbled into the well? _____

4) How did the fox get out of the well?

   He jumped out. ☐   He climbed out. ☐   He stood on the goat's back. ☐

5) Do you think the fox was a good friend to the goat? Why?

   _____

   _____

6) Find these words in the story and circle them. Read them to someone.

   fox   well   fell   high   goat   jump   jumped   out

Name _____

The fox and the goat

Once there was a fox who drank water from a well. One day he leaned over so far to get the water that he fell in. The wall of the well was too high for him to get out again.

Along came a goat. 'Why are you down in the well?' the goat asked the fox.

'Because the water is so cool and tasty,' said the fox. 'Why don't you jump down into the well and taste it?'

The goat jumped into the well. As soon as he reached the bottom, the fox jumped on his back and climbed out.

'Ha, ha, ha,' laughed the fox. 'You should look before you leap, friend goat!' And off he ran.

1) Where did the fox drink his water from? _____

2) How did he reach the water? _____

3) What happened to the fox that day? _____

_____

4) Why didn't he get out of the well? _____

_____

5) Who came along next? _____

6) The fox said he was in the well because:

He had fallen in. ☐   The water was cool and tasty. ☐

He was having a swim. ☐   He liked it in the well. ☐

7) How did the fox get the goat to jump into the well? _____

_____

8) What does 'look before you leap' mean? _____

_____

9) Find these words in the text and circle them. Read them to someone.

drank   well   leaned   high   cool   tasty   reached   leap

Name _____

The fox and the goat

Once there was a fox who always drank his water from a well in the ground.

One day he leaned over so far to get the water that he fell in. Try as he might, the wall of the well was too high for him to climb back out again.

Along came a goat. 'What are you doing down in the well?' the curious goat asked the fox.

'Well,' said the fox. 'I am enjoying the cool, tasty water. 'Why don't you jump down into the well and taste it?'

Without stopping to think, the foolish goat jumped into the well. As soon as he reached the bottom, the fox jumped on his back and scrambled to the top.

Looking down at the unhappy goat, the fox laughed. 'Ha, ha, ha! You should look before you leap, friend goat!' And off he ran.

1) What did the fox have to do to get water from the well? _____

_____

2) What happened to him? _____

3) Why couldn't he get out of the well? _____

4) What do the words 'try as he might' tell you? _____

_____

5) Why does it say the goat was curious?

_____

_____

6) Why does it say the goat was foolish?

_____

_____

7) How did the fox get out of the well? _____

_____

8) Do you think one of the animals played a trick on the other? Which one? How?

_____

_____

9) Read these words and find them in the text. Read them to someone.

Name _____

Ducklings at Home Pond

A new neighbour

Someone new had come to live at Home Pond. It was a duck.

The duck sat on a nest that was full of eggs. She waited for them to hatch.

Mrs Duck was very lonely sitting on her nest. All the other ducks were swimming and rushing about but they all left her by herself.

The eggs hatch

One day something wonderful happened. There was a cracking sound from one of the eggs. Then another. Then another.

'Peep! Peep!' came a sound. 'Peep! Peep!' came another sound. Suddenly there came 'Peep! Peep!' from six different places.

The eggs had hatched!

1) Fill in the missing words:

Someone ___ ___ ___ had come to live at Home Pond.

The duck sat on a ___ ___ ___ ___.

The nest was full of ___ ___ ___ ___.

Mrs ___ ___ ___ ___ was very lonely.

2) Find a subheading in the story. What does it tell you?

_____

3) What do you think was making the sound 'Peep! Peep!'?

_____

4) How many eggs do you think hatched?

four ☐   six ☐   ten ☐   twelve ☐

5) How do you know? _____

6) Find these words in the story. Circle them and read them to someone.

eggs   nest   other   sound   places   hatched

Name _____

Ducklings at Home Pond

The Frog family could see that someone new had come to
live at Home Pond. It was a duck.

A new neighbour

The duck sat on a nest that was full of eggs. She waited for them to hatch.

Mrs Duck was very lonely. All of the other ducks were swimming and rushing
about but they all left her alone by herself.

The eggs hatch

One day a cracking sound came from one of the eggs. Then another.

'Peep! Peep!' came a sound. 'Peep! Peep!' came another sound.

Suddenly there came 'Peep! Peep!' from six different places.

Then six little ducklings thrust their heads out of the shells and looked at the
world around them. 'How big the world is,' they said.

1) Find these words in the story. Circle them and read them to someone.

new   nest   alone   cracking   hatched   thrust

2) Find two subheadings in the text. What do they say?

1. _____

2. _____

3) Why was the duck sitting on her nest?

_____

4) What was she waiting for?

Visitors. ☐   To go for a swim. ☐   To make new friends. ☐   The eggs to hatch. ☐

5) How did she feel?

happy ☐   sad ☐   contented ☐   lonely ☐

6) What was making the crackling sound? _____

7) Which words tell you which bits of the ducklings came out of the shells first?

_____

8) What did the ducklings think of the world?

_____

·· ······

Name _____

Ducklings at Home Pond

The Frog family could see that someone new had come
to live at Home Pond. It was a duck.

A new neighbour

The duck sat on a nest that was full of eggs. She waited for them to hatch.

Mrs Duck was very lonely sitting on her nest. She didn't know any of her
neighbours. She had no visitors. All of the other ducks were swimming and
rushing about but they all left her alone by herself.

The eggs hatch

One day there was a cracking sound from one of the eggs. Then another.
Suddenly there came 'Peep! Peep!' from six different places. The eggs had
hatched! Six little featherless ducklings thrust their heads out of the shells and
looked at the world around them. 'How big the world is,' they said.

1) Circle these words in the text and read them to someone.

    neighbour   lonely   visitors   rushing   cracking   hatched   thrust

2) Find two subheadings in the text. What do they say?

    1. _____ 2. _____

3) Which words tell you how the duck felt?

    _____

    _____

4) What did the other ducks like to do? _____

5) How do you know the eggs were hatching?

    Because it was time. ☐   Because of the cracking sound. ☐

    Because the duck had sat on the eggs a long time. ☐

6) What did the ducklings look like when they came out of their shells? Which word tells you this?

    _____

7) Which words tell you which bits of the ducklings came out of the eggs first?

    _____

8) What kind of world did the ducklings think they had come into?

    _____

Name _____

Telling fiction from non-fiction

How can you tell fiction from non-fiction?

Fiction is text that is made up or pretend. Non-fiction is text about facts that are real or true.

Fiction includes stories, poems, plays and comics.

Non-fiction includes reference books, maps and newspapers.

Rita Rabbit is going shopping.

Rabbits need fresh, clean water every day.

"Night, night. Sleep tight," said Mum Rabbit.

This is _____   This is _____   This is _____

1) Fill in the missing words:

   Harry Potter is _____

   A dictionary is _____

   Fiction is text that is made up or _____

   Non-fiction is about _____ that are real or true.

2) Fiction is:
   stories ☐   plays ☐   poems ☐   comics ☐   all of these ☐

3) Non-fiction is:
   reference books ☐   maps ☐   newspapers ☐   all of these

4) Which do you most like to read?

   Fiction ☐   Non-fiction ☐

5) Why? _____

Name _____

Telling fiction from non-fiction

How can you tell fiction from non-fiction?

Fiction is text that is made up or pretend. Non-fiction is text about facts that are real or true.

Fiction includes stories, poems, plays and comics.

Non-fiction includes reference books, maps and newspapers.

Rita Rabbit is going shopping.

Rabbits need fresh, clean water every day.

"Night, night. Sleep tight," said Mum Rabbit.

1) Which of these are fiction?

stories ☐   plays ☐   newspapers ☐   poems ☐

2) Which of these are non-fiction?

maps ☐   reference books ☐   comics ☐   newspapers ☐

3) In picture A, which clues tell you whether the text is fiction or non-fiction?

_____

4) In picture B, which clues tell you whether the text is fiction or non-fiction?

_____

5) In picture C, what does the text tell you?

_____

6) Why do you think you need to know the difference between fiction and non-fiction?

Because it helps you to learn. ☐

Because it gives you good ideas. ☐

Because you can find out about rabbits. ☐

Because it helps you to choose the right book at the right time. ☐

Name _____

Telling fiction from non-fiction

How can you tell fiction from non-fiction?

Fiction is text that is made up or pretend. It is based on imagination and helps you to develop lots of ideas. Fiction includes stories, poems, plays and comics.

Non-fiction is text about facts that are real or true. It is good for finding out about things, for learning facts and for knowing how things work, where things come from and how things came to be. Non-fiction includes reference books, maps and newspapers.

Rita Rabbit is going shopping.

Rabbits need fresh, clean water every day.

"Night, night. Sleep tight," said Mum Rabbit.

This is _____   This is _____   This is _____

1) Which words in the text tell you what fiction is? Circle them in red.

2) Which words in the text tell you what non-fiction is? Circle them in blue.

3) On another sheet of paper, give three examples of texts that are fiction and three examples of texts that are non-fiction.

4) Which of these titles best fits each book? Write A, B or C:

   Rabbit family day ☐   Looking after pet rabbits ☐

   A trip to town ☐

5) What does fiction help you to do?

   Learn stories ☐   Learn poems ☐   Develop your imagination ☐

6) What does non-fiction help you to do?

   Learn facts ☐   Write good stories ☐   Write good poems ☐

7) Why do you think you need to know the difference between fiction and non-fiction?

   _____

   _____

   _____

Name _____

Easy-peasy concertina book

What you need:

| paper | sticky tape | card | scissors | writing tools |

What to do:

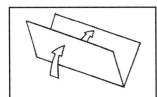 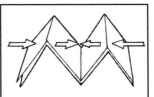 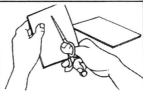 

Fold the paper in half along its length, to make it strong.

Fold the paper in an even number of parts. These will be the pages.

Cut two pieces of card the same size as the parts.

Tape one piece of card to each end for the covers.

Write your text on the paper.

Write the title on the front cover.

Write a blurb on the back cover.

Share your book.

1) Fill in the missing words:

You need ___ ___ ___ ___ ___ to fold.

You need ___ ___ ___ ___ ___ ___ ___ ___ to cut.

You need sticky ___ ___ ___ ___ to stick.

You need ___ ___ ___ ___ to write and draw.

2) What goes on the front cover of your book? _____

3) What goes on the back cover of your book? _____

4) What goes on the pages of your book? _____

5) Has this helped you to make a good book? _____

6) Think of some things you could write about in your book.

7) Share your book with friends.

Name _____

Easy-peasy concertina book

What you need:

 paper
 sticky tape
 card
 scissors
 writing tools

What to do:

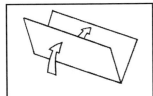
Fold the paper in half along its length, to make it strong.

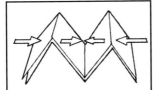
Fold the paper in an even number of parts. These will be the pages.

Cut two pieces of card the same size as the parts.

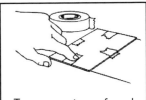
Tape one piece of card to each end for the covers.

Write your text on the paper.

Write the title on the front cover.

Write a blurb on the back cover.

Share your book.

1) What kind of writing is this?

a story ☐   a play ☐   instructions ☐   a recount ☐

2) How many things do you need to collect to make the book? _____

3) When you have everything you need, what should you do first?

_____

4) How can you make the front cover and back cover different from the pages?

_____

5) Follow the instructions to make the book. The instructions are:

easy to follow ☐   difficult to follow ☐

6) Why do you think this? _____

_____

7) Share your book with a friend. Tell the friend how to make a book like yours.

....

Name _____

Easy-peasy concertina book

What you need:

paper

sticky tape

card

scissors

writing tools

What to do:

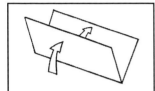
Fold the paper in half along its length, to make it strong.

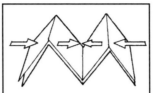
Fold the paper in an even number of parts. These will be the pages.

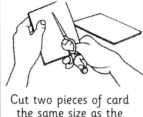
Cut two pieces of card the same size as the parts.

Tape one piece of card to each end for the covers.

Write your text on the paper.

Write the title on the front cover.

Write a blurb on the back cover.

Share your book.

1) What kind of writing is this?

a recipe ☐ a story ☐ a play ☐ a poem ☐ instructions ☐ a recount ☐

2) When you have everything you need, what should you do first? Say why.

_____

3) How can you make the front cover and back cover different from the pages?

_____

4) Do you think having 'What you need' and 'What to do' is a good way of doing this kind of writing? Say why. _____

_____

5) Follow the instructions to make the book. Do you think the instructions are:

easy to follow ☐ difficult to follow ☐

Why do you think this? _____

7) Do the diagrams help? If so, how? _____

_____

Name _____

The new book

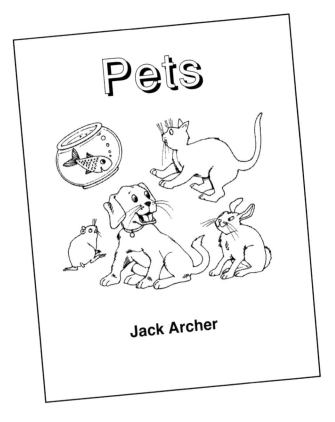

Jack Archer

Contents

All you need to know to look after your pets.

With 75 colour illustrations.

Different kinds of pets – information about feeding, grooming and exercising.

1) Fill in the missing words:

The book is called ___ ___ ___ ___.

It tells you how to ___ ___ ___ ___ after them.

You can find out about c ___ ___ ___.

You can find out about d ___ ___ ___.

You can find out about _____

There are _____ colour pictures in the book.

2) Where does the chapter about rabbits start?

_____

3) Where does the chapter about fish start?

_____

4) Would this book tell you how to look after an elephant? Why?

_____

Name _____

The new book

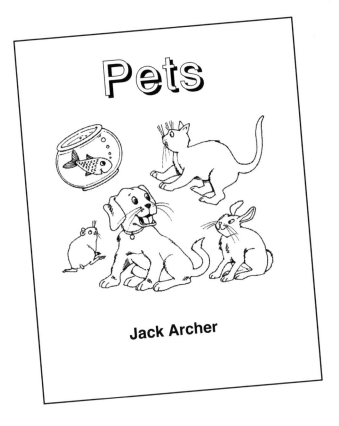

Pets

Jack Archer

Contents

Cats	4
Dogs	12
Hamsters	20
Rabbits	24
Fish	28
Index	32

All you need to know about your pets.

With 75 colour illustrations.

Different kinds of pets – information about feeding, grooming and exercising.

1) What is the title of the new book? _____

2) What kind of animals does it tell you about?

wild animals ☐ zoo animals ☐ farm animals ☐ pets ☐

3) How many different types of animal does it have in it? _____

4) Where will you find the chapter on rabbits? _____

5) What would you find out about looking after a pet? Which words tell you this?

_____

6) How would you know the book has pictures in it without looking through it?

_____

7) Do you think this book is:

a story book ☐ a dictionary ☐ a reference book ☐ a directory ☐

8) Name three different animals the book tells you about.

_____

Name _____

The new book

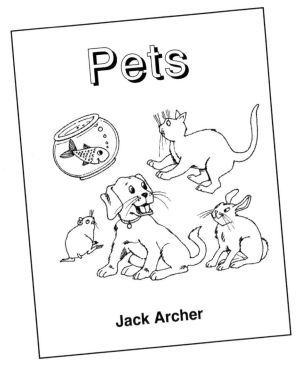

Contents

Cats	4
Dogs	12
Hamsters	20
Rabbits	24
Fish	28
Index	32

All you need to know about your pets.

With 75 colour illustrations.

Different kinds of pets – information about feeding, grooming and exercising.

1) What kind of book do you think this is? _____

2) Does it have pictures? Yes ☐ No ☐

   How do you know? _____

3) Would you learn all about giraffes in this book?   Yes ☐   No ☐

   How do you know? _____

4) How many pages do you think the book has?

   about 60 ☐   about 102 ☐   32 ☐   26 ☐

5) What will you find on the last page? _____

6) Who wrote the book? _____

7) What is its title? _____

8) What kind of information will you find inside it? _____

   _____

9) If you are interested in rabbits, which chapter will you look at? _____

   _____

10) What will you find information on in pages 20–23? _____

11) In this book will you find:

   a setting? ☐   characters? ☐   a plot? ☐   information? ☐